That's Life Snoopy

selected cartoons from
Thompson Is In Trouble, Charlie Brown Vol. 2

Charles M. Schulz

CORONET BOOKS
Hodder Fawcett, London

First published by Fawcett Publications Inc., New York.
Reprinted by arrangement with Holt, Rinehart and Winston, Inc.

Coronet Edition 1978
Second Impression 1978

Printed and bound in Great Britain for Hodder Fawcett Ltd., Mill Road, Dunton Green, Sevenoaks, Kent (Editorial Office: 47 Bedford Square, London, WC1 3DP) by C. Nicholls & Company Ltd The Philips Park Press, Manchester

ISBN 0 340 22313 8

THAT'S
LIFE,
SNOOPY

YOU HAVE NO IDEA HOW IMPORTANT IT IS FOR A GIRL TO GET PRESENTS
IF NO ONE GIVES HER PRESENTS, HER LIFE HAS NO MEANING!
AREN'T YOU INTERESTED IN THE MEANING OF LIFE?
SCHULZ

YOU KNOW WHAT BEETHOVEN NEVER HAD?
BEETHOVEN NEVER HAD GIRLS HANGING ON HIS PIANO BUGGING HIM ABOUT SENDING THEM PRESENTS!
HE DIDN'T?
POOR BEETHOVEN!
SCHULZ

IF A BOY NEVER SENDS A GIRL FLOWERS, HE ROBS HIMSELF OF ONE OF THE GREAT JOYS OF LIFE...
THIEF! ROBBER!!
SCHULZ

To Whom It May Concern;
Dear Whom,
SCHULZ

?
PROBABLY A SCARECROW

THIS IS KIND OF INTERESTING... WOODSTOCK SAYS HE SORT OF FIGURED IT WAS A SCARECROW..

HE SAYS THAT HE KNEW ALL ALONG IT WASN'T A REAL HUMAN BEING BECAUSE MOST HUMAN BEINGS ARE NOT THAT FOND OF STANDING FOR SUCH A LENGTH OF TIME IN THE HOT SUN...

HE SAYS THE FACT THAT THE CLOTHES ARE OUT OF STYLE ALSO MADE HIM A LITTLE SUSPICIOUS..

BLEAH!

WOODSTOCK WOULD HAVE MADE A GOOD CROW!
SCHULZ

GO STRAIGHT OUT, SNOOPY, AND THEN CUT LEFT... I'LL FAKE A RUN, AND PASS IT...
DO YOU THINK THAT'S A GOOD PLAY?
SMAK!
HE THINKS IT'S A GOOD PLAY!
SCHULZ

ALL RIGHT, TEAM, LET'S PAY ATTENTION
WE'RE HERE TODAY TO TRY TO EVALUATE OUR PERFORMANCES ON THE FIELD...EACH OF US CAN STAND A LITTLE IMPROVEMENT...
EACH OF US CAN LEARN SOMETHING IF WE'RE WILLING TO ACCEPT CRITICISM...
YOUR NOSE IS TOO BIG!
SCHULZ

WELL, HERE I AM AGAIN FOR "SHOW AND TELL"
AND GUESS WHAT I'VE BROUGHT TODAY! I HAVE THINGS IN HERE TO THRILL YOU AND CHILL YOU! I HAVE THINGS IN HERE TO FILL YOU WITH FEAR, WITH TERROR, WITH HORROR! I HAVE THINGS IN HERE TO...
...YES, MA'AM?
ALL THE LIFE HAS GONE OUT OF "SHOW AND TELL"
SCHULZ

Science Report;
"Forest Strangers"
Our wild life and our trees are protected by brave and dedicated men.
These men live by themselves in towers and are called Forest Strangers.
I WONDER IF I SHOULD INCLUDE AN EXPLANATION OF HOW THEY GOT THAT NAME..
PROBABLY NOT
SCHULZ

!
A WORM TWO FEET LONG? THAT'S RIDICULOUS!
SCHULZ

WOODSTOCK GIVES BORING PARTIES!
SCHULZ

COLUMNIST
HERE'S ONE FROM IOWA...AND HERE'S ONE FROM PENNSYLVANIA..
Advice For Dog Owners
type type type
"DEAR SIR, I HAVE A DOG WHO CONTINUALLY SCRATCHES HIS EARS...WHAT SHOULD I DO? SIGNED, 'WONDERING'"
Dear Wondering, What I'm wondering is how you can be so dumb! Take your dog to the vet right away, stupid.
type type type type

"DEAR SIR, WE HAVE THREE PUPPIES WHO HAVE ENLARGED JOINTS AND ARE LAME... WHAT DO YOU THINK CAUSED THIS, AND WHAT SHOULD WE DO? SIGNED, DOG OWNER'"
Dear Dog Owner, Why don't you take up rock collecting? You're too stupid to be a dog owner. In the meantime, call your vet immediately.
type
type
type
type
'DEAR SIR, MY DOG HAS BEEN COUGHING LATELY... WHAT SHOULD I DO? SIGNED, 'CONFUSED'"
Dear Confused, You're not confused, you're just not very smart. Now, you get that dog to the vet right away before I come over and punch you in the nose!
type
type
type
I WRITE A VERY FIRM COLUMN!
SCHULZ

WHAT A GREAT TITLE!
Toodle-oo, Caribou! A Tale of the Frozen North
One morning, Joe Eskimo went out to his barn to milk his polar cow. As he walked through the barn, tiny polar mice scampered across the frozen floor.
HMM..

I HATE TO TELL YOU THIS, BUT THERE ISN'T SUCH A THING AS A POLAR COW..
THERE ISN'T?
OKAY, SCRATCH THE POLAR COW..
THERE AREN'T SUCH THINGS AS POLAR MICE, EITHER...
THERE AREN'T?
OKAY, SCRATCH THE POLAR MICE... SIGH..
SOME OF MY BEST NOVELS NEVER GET OFF THE GROUND..
SCHULZ

type
type
type
type
Toodle-oo, Caribou!
A Tale of the Frozen North
The stall was empty!
"Someone has stolen my polar cow!" shouted Joe Eskimo.
"This is the work of Joe Jacket, who hates me!"

MAY I SEE HOW YOUR NEW NOVEL IS COMING ALONG?
BE MY GUEST..
"JOE ESKIMO AND JOE JACKET WERE RIVALS FOR THE HEART OF SALLY SNOW WHO LIVED SOUTH OF THE ICEBERG....JOE ESKIMO THOUGHT BACK TO THE NIGHT HE FIRST SHOOK HER HAND"
"'I THINK YOU ARE VERY NICE,' HE HAD TOLD HER, AND THEY SHOOK HANDS."
THEY SHOOK HANDS?
I THINK YOUR LOVE SCENE NEEDS A LITTLE SOMETHING..
I ALWAYS GET SO EMBARRASSED..
SCHULZ

I SIGNED UP FOR A NEW COURSE TODAY
IT'S CALLED "INTRODUCTION TO MATH"
IS IT HARD?
NOT AT ALL..
I JUST WALKED RIGHT IN, AND SAID, "HOW DO YOU DO, MATH!"
SCHULZ

MY FAVORITE HOCKEY TEAM DIDN'T DO TOO WELL LAST YEAR...
THIS SEASON, HOWEVER, THEY HAVE HIGH HOPES..
DID THEY GET SOME NEW PLAYERS?
NO, THEY BOUGHT A NEW PUCK!
SCHULZ

HERE... A MESSAGE JUST CAME FOR YOU..
A MESSAGE?
IT MUST BE FROM THE "HEAD BEAGLE"... IT'S IN CODE!
SCHULZ

YOU GOT A CODED MESSAGE FROM THE HEAD BEAGLE?
CAN YOU READ IT? HAVE YOU FIGURED IT OUT? WHAT DOES IT SAY?
I CAN'T BELIEVE IT...
"THOMPSON IS IN TROUBLE!"
THOMPSON?! WHO IS THOMPSON?
THAT STUPID THOMPSON! HE'S DONE IT AGAIN!!
SCHULZ

WHAT IN THE WORLD IS THIS?
SNOOPY GOT A MESSAGE FROM THE HEAD BEAGLE... IT'S IN CODE...
WHAT DOES IT SAY?
IT SAYS, "THOMPSON IS IN TROUBLE!"
FOR A JOB LIKE THIS, I HAVE TO PUT ON MY FAMOUS DISGUISE...
THAT STUPID THOMPSON! THE LAST TIME THIS HAPPENED, HE ALMOST GOT US ALL KILLED...
SCHULZ

ISN'T HE GOING TO SAY GOODBY?
WHEN YOU LEAVE ON AN ASSIGNMENT FOR THE HEAD BEAGLE, YOU DON'T HAVE TIME TO SAY GOODBY!
RIGHT!
"THOMPSON IS IN TROUBLE!" THAT MEANS I'VE GOT TO GET TO HIM BEFORE "THEY" DO...
THIS REMINDS ME OF THE "MOROCCAN AFFAIR"... THAT WAS A NASTY PIECE OF BUSINESS...
THAT STUPID THOMPSON...HE NEVER WANTED TO TAKE ANY ADVICE..NOW, MAYBE IT'S TOO LATE..
SCHULZ

THOMPSON ?
THOMPSON ?
HMM...THERE'S A LITTLE RESTAURANT THAT LOOKS FULL OF SHADY TYPES...
MAYBE THE WAITRESS KNOWS THOMPSON...I'LL GO IN, AND SLYLY STRIKE UP A CONVERSATION WITH HER...
HI, SWEETIE!
SCHULZ

UH...IT'S LIKE THIS, SWEETIE...
I'M KIND OF LOOKING FOR A CHARACTER NAMED THOMPSON, SEE, AND I SORTA NEED YOUR HELP
HE'S ABOUT FOURTEEN INCHES... CARRIES A GOOD STRAIGHT LINE, HARKS TO THE TRACK, HAS A QUICK CLAIMING MOUTH RIGHT IN THE GROUND AND HAS A GOOD PEDIGREE
SHE KNOWS HIM!!
SCHULZ

THAT WAITRESS SAID SHE SAW THOMPSON HEADING NORTH OF TOWN..
THAT STUPID THOMPSON! THIS IS JUST THE SORT OF THING I KNEW HE'D DO!
I SHOULD BE BACK IN THE RESTAURANT QUAFFING ROOT BEERS WITH THAT WAITRESS... I THINK SHE KIND OF LIKED ME..
NOW, IT'S RAINING, AND I'M GETTING ALL WET AND I'M PROBABLY LOST... THAT STUPID THOMPSON!!

THOMPSON?
THOMPSON, WHERE ARE YOU?
THOMPSON?
!
TOO LATE!
POOR THOMPSON!
SCHULZ

Report to the Head Beagle
Subject: Our Beagle in the field, Thompson.
Subject attempted to subdue ten thousand rabbits by himself. End came quickly.
Rabbit-tat-tat, and it was all over!
SCHULZ

POOR THOMPSON
I WAS SORRY TO HEAR ABOUT THOMPSON..
I SUPPOSE YOU'LL NEVER KNOW WHAT REALLY HAPPENED, WILL YOU?
ON THE CONTRARY
I KNOW EXACTLY WHAT HAPPENED...
THOSE RABBITS MADE HIM AN OFFER HE COULDN'T REFUSE!
SCHULZ

CHARLIE BROWNNNN
I'LL HOLD THE FOOTBALL, CHARLIE BROWN, AND YOU COME RUNNING UP, AND KICK IT..
I CAN'T
I NEVER DO ANYTHING WITHOUT CONSULTING MY PSYCHIATRIST...
WELL, YOU GO TALK WITH YOUR PSYCHIATRIST, AND SEE WHAT YOU WANT TO DO...OKAY?
PSYCHIATRIC HELP 5¢
THE DOCTOR IS IN
I HAVE A STRANGE PROBLEM

THERE'S THIS GIRL, SEE, AND SHE'S ALWAYS TRYING TO GET ME TO KICK THIS FOOTBALL, BUT SHE ALSO ALWAYS PULLS IT AWAY AND I LAND ON MY BACK AND KILL MYSELF...
SHE SOUNDS LIKE AN INTERESTING GIRL...SORT OF A FUN TYPE...

I GET THE IMPRESSION THAT YOU HAVE A REAL NEED TO KICK THIS FOOTBALL...I THINK YOU SHOULD TRY IT!
I THINK YOU SHOULD TRY IT BECAUSE IN MEDICAL TERMS, YOU HAVE WHAT WE CALL THE "NEED TO NEED TO TRY IT"

I'M GLAD I TALKED WITH MY PSYCHIATRIST BECAUSE THIS YEAR I'M GONNA KICK THAT BALL CLEAR TO THE MOON!

AUGH!

WHAM

UNFORTUNATELY, CHARLIE BROWN, YOUR AVERAGE PSYCHIATRIST KNOWS VERY LITTLE ABOUT KICKING FOOTBALLS
SCHULZ

Z
SCHULZ

WELL, AT LEAST THEY CAN RUN FASTER...
HOW CAN YOU TALK TO SOMEONE WHO KEEPS SAYING, "AU CONTRAIRE"?
SCHULZ

I GOT SIX COMPLIMENTS TODAY...
FANTASTIC!
IT'S NOT OFTEN YOU CAN GET SIX COMPLIMENTS IN ONE DAY
TWO OF THEM WERE EVEN SINCERE!
SCHULZ

I WORRIED ABOUT THIS TEST ALL NIGHT..
I WORRIED AND WORRIED AND WORRIED...
SO WHAT HAPPENED?
I GOT AN "A"
I WASTED A GOOD WORRY!
SCHULZ

ALL RIGHT, NOW THIS NEXT LETTER WILL BE TO...
WHAT?
SEED BREAK!
SCHULZ

DEAR SIR...
IS THERE REALLY SUCH A THING AS A "WORM BREAK"?
SCHULZ

?
"FEAR OF FALLING LEAVES."...
WHEN WE GET HOME, I'LL HAVE
TO LOOK THAT ONE UP...
SCHULZ

HMM..

IT SAYS HERE THAT THE HUMMINGBIRD IS THE ONLY WINGED CREATURE THAT CAN FLAP HIS WINGS FAST ENOUGH TO BE ABLE TO HOVER MOTIONLESS IN THE AIR...

THAT'S VERY INTERESTING
KLUNK!
ONE-TENTH OF A SECOND IS NOT A HOVER!
SCHULZ

YES, MA'AM...WE'D LIKE TO BORROW THE LATEST BOOK BY MISS HELEN SWEETSTORY..
BANNED?!!
IT'S BEEN BANNED FROM THE SCHOOL LIBRARY! I CAN'T BELIEVE IT!
HOW COULD ANYONE BAN SUCH A NEAT BOOK AS "THE SIX BUNNY-WUNNIES FREAK OUT"?
SCHULZ

WHY WOULD THEY BAN MISS SWEETSTORY'S BOOK FROM THE SCHOOL LIBRARY?
I CAN'T BELIEVE IT.. I JUST CAN'T BELIEVE IT!
MAYBE THERE ARE SOME THINGS IN HER BOOK THAT WE DON'T UNDERSTAND...
IN THAT CASE, THEY SHOULD ALSO BAN MY MATH BOOK!

YES, MA'AM, WE'D LIKE TO SEE THE PRINCIPAL IF HE'S NOT TOO BUSY...
WELL, IT'S KIND OF A PERSONAL MATTER... YES, MA'AM... WE'RE STUDENTS HERE..
WHAT DID YOU THINK WE WERE, ENCYCLOPEDIA SALESMEN?
PRINCIPAL'S OFFICE
WHATEVER HAPPENED TO GOOD OLD-FASHIONED TACT ?!
SCHULZ

HOW CAN I WRITE MY ENGLISH THEME ON MISS SWEETSTORY'S NEW BOOK IF IT'S BEEN BANNED FROM OUR LIBRARY?
MAYBE YOU'LL HAVE TO WRITE ABOUT SOMETHING ELSE...
HOW ABOUT GRAPES?
I COULD WRITE ABOUT HOW EXCITING IT IS WHEN THE GRAPE BOATS COME SAILING INTO THE ARBOR...
THERE MUST BE SOMETHING WRONG WITH ME..I NEVER KNOW WHAT TO SAY...
SCHULZ

SCHOOL CROSSING
I'M MAD, CHARLIE BROWN!
THEY'VE BANNED HELEN SWEETSTORY'S BOOK FROM OUR SCHOOL LIBRARY, AND I CAN'T FIND OUT WHY!!
I'M SO MAD I FEEL LIKE SUING THE SCHOOL BOARD! I THINK I WOULD, TOO, IF I HAD AN ATTORNEY...
BEFORE I TAKE ANY CASE, I HAVE TO KNOW WHERE TO SEND THE BILL!
SCHULZ

ALL RIGHT, ATTORNEY, I'LL EXPLAIN OUR PROBLEM, AND YOU TELL ME IF WE HAVE A CASE..
"IMPOSSIBILITY IS AN EXCUSE IN LAW"
OUR SCHOOL LIBRARY HAS BANNED A CERTAIN BOOK, SEE, AND WE WANT TO FIND OUT WHY...
"ARREST THE DEBTOR TO SATISFY A JUDGMENT"
NOW, IT'S NOT SO MUCH A MATTER OF THE BOOK ITSELF AS WHY WE...
Z
SIGH
SCHULZ

Dear Miss Sweetstory,
I suppose you have heard about the banning of your book from our library.

Well, I just wanted you to know that I am fighting for you. I have even hired an attorney.

"THE SUPPRESSING OF EVIDENCE OUGHT ALWAYS TO BE TAKEN FOR THE STRONGEST EVIDENCE!"

Such as he is.

SCHULZ

OKAY, ATTORNEY, LET'S MAKE A FEW PHONE CALLS, AND SEE WHAT WE CAN FIND OUT..
"WE KNOW THAT THE LAW IS GOOD IF A MAN USE IT LAWFULLY"
HELLO, SCHOOL BOARD?
I WONDER IF JOHN DOE OR RICHARD ROE WILL BE IN COURT... I HATE CASES THAT DON'T HAVE JOHN DOE OR RICHARD ROE..
YES, I'D LIKE TO SPEAK TO THE HEAD OF THE SCHOOL BOARD, PLEASE..
"THE CLIENT CARES LITTLE FOR A 'BEAUTIFUL' CASE"
SCHULZ

I'M SURE THE LIBRARIAN DIDN'T BAN THE BOOK, CHARLIE BROWN
I'M GLAD
AND I DON'T THINK IT WAS THE PRINCIPAL..
I'M GLAD
I'M SURE IT WAS THE SCHOOL BOARD, AND GUESS WHO'S ON THE SCHOOL BOARD...
YOUR OWN PEDIATRICIAN, CHARLIE BROWN!
SCHULZ

YOU WANT ME TO TALK TO MY OWN DOCTOR ABOUT MISS SWEETSTORY'S BOOK?
WHY NOT? HE'S ON THE SCHOOL BOARD, ISN'T HE? HE WAS THE ONE WHO BANNED HER BOOK!
DO PEOPLE REALLY TALK TO DOCTORS?
OF COURSE, CHARLIE BROWN.. EVERY DAY...
DO THE DOCTORS LISTEN?
SCHULZ

YES, MA'AM, I'D LIKE TO TALK TO THE DOCTOR...
NO, I FEEL FINE... I'D JUST LIKE TO TALK TO HIM FOR A MINUTE...
I SEE...
IF I GO BACK OUTSIDE AND CATCH A COLD, THEN MAY I TALK TO HIM?
SCHULZ

GOOD AFTERNOON, DOCTOR..
I'M FINE, THANK YOU... YES, I THINK I'VE BEEN FEELING VERY WELL LATELY...
I APPRECIATE YOUR SEEING ME LIKE THIS...
I WAS AFRAID YOU MIGHT THINK IT WAS A WASTE OF TIME TALKING TO A WELL PERSON..
SCHULZ

YOU'RE MY DOCTOR, SIR, AND I RESPECT YOU...
HOWEVER, I'VE COME TO SEE YOU BECAUSE I HAVE TO KNOW WHY YOU AND THE SCHOOL BOARD BANNED "THE SIX BUNNY WUNNIES FREAK OUT" FROM OUR LIBRARY...
KLUNK!!
!
SOMEHOW, YOU NEVER EXPECT A DOCTOR TO FAINT...
SCHULZ

NURSE! HURRY!! THE DOCTOR HAS FAINTED!
IS HE ALL RIGHT? WAS IT SOMETHING I SAID?
I SEE... I UNDERSTAND
HE'S A GREAT PEDIATRICIAN, BUT CHILDREN MAKE HIM NERVOUS!
SCHULZ

OKAY, I HOPE YOU'RE SATISFIED... I TALKED WITH MY PEDIATRICIAN..
ACTUALLY, HE'S A VERY SENSITIVE PERSON...EVEN THOUGH HE FAINTS A LOT.... HE ADMITTED THAT HE'S NEVER REALLY READ MISS SWEETSTORY'S BOOK...
HE SAID HE ONLY READS MEDICAL JOURNALS...
ALTHOUGH SOMETIMES THE PICTURES UPSET HIM
SCHULZ

I'M AWAKE!!

PEPPERMINT PATTY LOVES

LIFE IS LIKE A BRACELET, CHUCK

LIKE A WHAT?

LIFE IS LIKE A BRACELET... IT HAS LITTLE JEWELS AROUND IT WHICH ARE LIKE THE LITTLE BRIGHT MOMENTS THAT COME ALONG IN OUR LIVES EVERY NOW AND THEN...

DO YOU FEEL THAT THIS HAS BEEN ONE OF THOSE BRIGHT MOMENTS, CHUCK? DO YOU FEEL THAT THIS HOUR WE HAVE HAD TOGETHER HAS BEEN LIKE A DIAMOND SET IN A BRACELET?
DO YOU FEEL THAT WAY, CHUCK? IF YOU DO, YOU SHOULD TELL ME..
WHY, YES...I THINK YOU'RE RIGHT.. LIFE IS VERY MUCH LIKE A COLLAR..
NOT A COLLAR, CHUCK.. A BRACELET!!!
SPEAKING OF COLLARS, SWEETIE.. I'M AN EXPERT!
I REMEMBER ONCE BACK ABOUT FIVE YEARS AGO... I SAID THE RIGHT THING..
SCHULZ

ROSEBUD!
IS THERE A LOT OF SWEARING IN THIS MOVIE?
I DON'T WANT TO SEE IT IF THERE'S A LOT OF SWEARING.. I'M NOT IN THE ARMY, YOU KNOW!
I LIKE TO THINK OF MYSELF AS A LADY, AND I REFUSE TO GO TO A MOVIE THAT HAS A LOT OF SWEARING...
WHY DO YOU TAKE ME TO MOVIES THAT HAVE A LOT OF SWEARING?
I'M NOT TAKING YOU TO THE MOVIES

WE'RE STANDING IN LINE TOGETHER, AREN'T WE?
THAT DOESN'T MEAN I'M TAKING YOU!

I GUESS IT DOESN'T, DOES IT? *SIGH*
ONE, PLEASE

FORGET IT!

WHAT ARE YOU DOING HOME? I THOUGHT YOU WENT TO THE MOVIES...

I AM... I'M WATCHING "CITIZEN KANE" FOR THE TENTH TIME!

?
SIGH
I HATE PLAYING "BAT"!
SCHULZ

?
THERE ARE A LOT OF THINGS IN THIS WORLD THAT WOODSTOCK HAS NEVER SEEN...ONE OF THEM IS A SALT LICK!
SCHULZ

flitter
HI, FEATHERS!
WOODSTOCK JUST HATES TO BE CALLED "FEATHERS"
!

HEE HEE HEE HEE HEE!
BANANA NOSE?!
HEE HEE HEE HEE HEE HEE
!
I GUESS IT'S BEST TO COME OUT EVEN...
SCHULZ

SOME MORNING I'M GOING TO GET UP REAL EARLY, AND WATCH THE SUN RISE...

ACTUALLY, AS YOU PROBABLY KNOW, THE SUN DOESN'T RISE.. THE EARTH TURNS...

SOME MORNING I'M GOING TO GET UP REAL EARLY, AND WATCH THE EARTH TURN...

SCHULZ

BETTY? YES, MA'AM.. I ADMIT IT...
I SIGNED MY ENGLISH REPORT "BETTY".
IT WASN'T MUCH OF A REPORT...
I CHANGED MY NAME TO PROTECT THE INNOCENT
SCHULZ

AH! A LETTER FROM MY PUBLISHER!
HMM..
Author Questionnaire; These questions are designed to prepare the media with information.
Author's name Snoopy
Residence Just a doghouse.
Phone unlisted.
Birth See records at Daisy Hill Puppy Farm.
Citizenship Papers misplaced. These things happen.

Reason for writing Book I wrote from a sense of need. I needed something to do. You can't just sleep all day long.

I was one of eight Beagles. We had a happy life. Lots to eat and a good cage, although looking out at the world through chicken wire can get to you after awhile.

Married Almost once, but that's a long story.

Schools and Colleges attended Obedience School dropout.

Suggestions for Promotion If you don't promote my book, I'll get another publisher so fast it will make your head spin.

I LIKE FILLING OUT QUESTIONNAIRES!

SCHULZ

IT'S MIGRATING TIME...
THIS IS THE TIME OF YEAR WHEN MILLIONS OF BIRDS ARE TAKING OFF FOR WARMER CLIMATES...
ALL BUT WOODSTOCK, WHO'S AFRAID OF GETTING MUGGED!
SIGH
SCHULZ

"SOME MIGRATING BIRDS ARE GUIDED BY A SINGLE STAR"
"OTHERS ARE GUIDED IN THEIR TRAVELS BY LINES OF MAGNETIC FORCE"
?
STILL OTHERS TALK A STUPID FRIEND INTO GOING ALONG, AND SHOWING THEM THE WAY!
SCHULZ

WHERE IN THE WORLD ARE THEY GOING?

I THINK THEY'RE MIGRATING

BEAGLES DON'T MIGRATE!

HEY, STUPID, HASN'T ANYONE EVER TOLD YOU BEAGLES DON'T MIGRATE?

I HATE BEING MOCKED BY LOW TYPES!

SCHULZ

WHAT I DON'T UNDERSTAND IS HOW WE KNOW WHEN WE'VE MIGRATED TO WHERE WE'RE MIGRATING...
DO WE JUST SUDDENLY SAY, "WE'RE HERE!" OR DOES SOMEONE SAY, "THIS IS IT!"? I HOPE NO ONE SHOUTS, "HEY, MAC!" I HATE IT WHEN SOMEONE SHOUTS, "HEY, MAC!"
I HATE NOT KNOWING WHERE I'M GOING OR WHAT I'M DOING!
LET'S FACE IT...MIGRATING IS FOR THE BIRDS!
SCHULZ

DO I KNOW WHAT YOU WOULD DO IF YOU HAD FORTY DOLLARS? NO, WHAT WOULD YOU DO IF YOU HAD FORTY DOLLARS?

BUY A FORTY-DOLLAR CANDY BAR!

HEE HEE HEE HEE HEE

I HATE JOKES LIKE THAT...I THINK THIS MIGRATING IS WARPING WOODSTOCK'S BRAIN!

SCHULZ

OKAY, FRIEND, THIS IS AS FAR AS I GO...
YOU CAN SORT OF MIGRATE HERE FOR THE WINTER...HAVE A GOOD TIME...I'LL SEE YOU IN THE SPRING...
I KNEW THIS WOULD HAPPEN!
SCHULZ

I KNEW THAT WOODSTOCK WOULD CHICKEN OUT!
* SIGH *
WE CAME ALL THIS WAY FOR NOTHING...NOW, HE WANTS TO GO HOME...IT SEEMS TO ME IF WE'VE COME THIS FAR, WE SHOULD AT LEAST LOCK AROUND A LITTLE.
* SIGH *
THERE'S NO REAL HURRY TO GET HOME...THAT ROUNDHEADED KID CAN GET ALONG WITHOUT ME..
BESIDES, I HAVE THREE WEEKS' SICK LEAVE COMING!
* SIGH *
SCHULZ

YOU KNOW WHERE WE ARE? WE'RE NEAR THE DAISY HILL PUPPY FARM!
I CAN SHOW WOODSTOCK WHERE I WAS BORN! WOW!! THIS IS GREAT! WHAT A THRILL THIS WILL BE FOR WOODSTOCK!
I CAN SHOW HIM MY OLD CAGE, AND WHERE WE ATE, AND WHERE WE PLAYED AND EVERYTHING!
WOODSTOCK WILL BE SO EXCITED!
YAWN!
SCHULZ

IT'S GONE!!
THE DAISY HILL PUPPY FARM IS GONE!
THEY'VE BUILT A SIX-STORY PARKING GARAGE! AAUGH! I CAN'T STAND IT!!
?
YOU STUPID PEOPLE!!
YOU'RE PARKING ON MY MEMORIES!!!
SCHULZ

HOW COULD THEY DO IT?!
HOW COULD THEY TEAR DOWN THE PLACE WHERE I WAS BORN, AND BUILD A SIX-STORY PARKING GARAGE?
WAIT A MINUTE!! MAYBE THAT WASN'T A SIX-STORY PARKING GARAGE...MAYBE IT WAS A HUGE MONUMENT ERECTED TO MARK THE PLACE OF MY BIRTH!
IT WAS A SIX-STORY PARKING GARAGE!
SCHULZ

Pay to the Order of Me!
money, money, money $ and more money
Linus Van Pelt

HA!! LOOK AT THAT!

IT'S STARTING TO SNOW, AND I'M **READY**!

I'M GOING TO BE THE FIRST KID IN THE NEIGHBORHOOD TO SHOVEL WALKS..

I'M GOING FROM HOUSE TO HOUSE, AND I'M GOING TO SHOVEL EVERY SIDEWALK AND DRIVEWAY THAT I CAN FIND!

WILL YOU MAKE A LOT OF MONEY?
YOU BET I'LL MAKE A LOT OF MONEY! AND YOU THINK I'LL SPEND IT RIGHT AWAY, DON'T YOU? WELL, I WON'T!
I'LL PROBABLY PUT IT ALL IN A SAVINGS ACCOUNT, AND JUST LIVE OFF THE INTEREST, OR MAYBE I'LL BUY AN ANNUITY PAYABLE AT AGE TWELVE, OR MAYBE I'LL INVEST IT ALL IN SOME MUTUAL FUNDS, OR EVEN BUY SOME STOCK IN ONE OF OUR LOCAL COMPANIES THAT SEEMS TO BE GETTING BIGGER, OR...
..OR MAYBE I'LL... I'LL...
I REMEMBER READING ABOUT ABRAHAM LINCOLN, AND HOW HE USED TO DO HIS HOMEWORK WITH A PIECE OF COAL ON THE BACK OF A SHOVEL...
FORGET IT!

FOR "SHOW AND TELL" TODAY, I HAVE A LITTLE SURPRISE...
I HAVE BROUGHT THE FIRST SNOWFLAKE OF THE YEAR! NOW, AS YOU MAY OR MAY NOT KNOW, SNOWFLAKES ARE...
DUE TO CIRCUMSTANCES BEYOND OUR CONTROL, THIS PORTION OF "SHOW AND TELL" HAS BEEN CANCELLED!
SCHULZ

I THINK IT WOULD BE VERY ROMANTIC IF SOMEDAY YOU GAVE ME A SINGLE PERFECT ROSE
OR A CARNATION...OR EVEN AN OLD DANDELION...
HOW ABOUT A HANDFUL OF CRAB GRASS?
I'LL TAKE IT!
SCHULZ

STUPID KID!
PSYCHIATRIC HELP 7¢
DREAMS SERVE A VERY USEFUL PURPOSE...
THE DOCTOR IS IN
PSYCHIATRIC HELP 7¢
THE DREAMS OF NIGHT PREPARE YOU FOR THE DAY THAT FOLLOWS..
THE DOCTOR IS IN
WHAT DOES THAT MEAN?
THE DOCTOR IS IN

IT'S AT NIGHT, CHARLIE BROWN, WHEN YOU'RE SLEEPING, THAT YOUR BRAIN IS REALLY WORKING...
THE DOCTOR IS IN
YOUR BRAIN IS TRYING TO SORT EVERYTHING OUT FOR YOU...
THE DOCTOR
IT'S TRYING TO MAKE YOU SEE YOURSELF AS YOU REALLY ARE..
THE DOCTOR
PSYCHIATRIC HELP 7¢
EVEN MY BRAIN IS AGAINST ME!
THE DOCTOR IS IN
SCHULZ

WOODSTOCK FEELS THAT EATING BREAD CRUMBS IS KIND OF DEGRADING...

SCHULZ

WOODSTOCK THINKS THAT IF YOU SIT IN A MAILBOX LONG ENOUGH, YOU'LL GET A CHRISTMAS CARD...HE'S SO NAIVE...HE JUST..
SCHULZ

English Theme
"The True Meaning
of Christmas."

To me, Christmas is
the joy of getting.

YOU MEAN 'GIVING'...CHRISTMAS IS THE JOY OF GIVING....

I DON'T HAVE THE SLIGHTEST IDEA WHAT YOU'RE TALKING ABOUT!

SCHULZ

Christmas is getting all you can get while the getting is good.
GIVING! THE ONLY REAL JOY IS GIVING!
LIKE, WOW!
SCHULZ

LET'S SEE NOW... HOW CAN I PUT THIS INTO WORDS?
WHAT I MEAN IS... WHAT I WANT TO SAY IS... HOW CAN I PUT IT INTO WORDS? WHAT I'M TRYING TO SAY IS...
POW!
RATS! I WAS HOPING SHE COULD PUT IT INTO WORDS...
SCHULZ

YOU HIT ME YESTERDAY, REMEMBER?
THEREFORE, I'VE DECIDED NOT TO GET YOU ANYTHING FOR CHRISTMAS THIS YEAR!
WHAT ARE YOU DOING??
TAKING BACK A HIT!
SCHULZ

YOU HAVE TO GIVE ME A CHRISTMAS PRESENT!
THAT'S THE CHRISTMAS RULE!! YOU CAN'T IGNORE THE CHRISTMAS RULE!!
I CAN DO ANYTHING I WANT! YOU HIT ME SO I'VE DECIDED NOT TO GIVE YOU ANYTHING FOR CHRISTMAS!
I MAY HAVE TO SUFFER MARTYRDOM...
SCHULZ

YOU HAVE TO GIVE ME A CHRISTMAS PRESENT! IT SAYS SO IN THE BIBLE!
YOU'RE BLUFFING...THE BIBLE SAYS NOTHING ABOUT GIVING CHRISTMAS PRESENTS!
IT DOESN'T?
YOU CAN'T BLUFF AN OLD THEOLOGIAN!
SIGH
SCHULZ

HERE IT IS!! I FOUND IT!
I FOUND THE WORD "SISTER" IN THE BIBLE!
THERE IT IS, RIGHT THERE! SEE? THERE'S THE WORD "SISTER" RIGHT THERE IN THE BIBLE!
SO?
THAT PROVES YOU HAVE TO GIVE ME A CHRISTMAS PRESENT!!!
OH, GOOD GRIEF!
SCHULZ

SO YOU FOUND THE WORD "SISTER" IN THE BIBLE...
WHAT DOES THAT PROVE?
IT PROVES I KNOW MORE ABOUT THE BIBLE THAN YOU THOUGHT!
DID YOU FIND IT IN THE OLD TESTAMENT OR IN THE NEW TESTAMENT?
THE WHAT?
AH, HA!
I MAY HAVE TO HIT HIM AGAIN!
SCHULZ

Season's Greetings
I'LL READ THE LIST, AND YOU CAN TELL ME WHAT YOU WANT TO DO..
DO YOU WANT TO SEND A CHRISTMAS CARD TO MILLIE?
NO, LET'S FORGET MILLIE...I DON'T THINK SHE REALLY LIKES ME..
HOW ABOUT THE O'HARAS?
I DON'T KNOW...IT'S KIND OF HARD TO DECIDE...

THERE'S TINA... HOW ABOUT TINA?
TINA LIKES ME, BUT I DON'T KNOW...
HOW ABOUT JANET?
WELL, MAYBE...
I KNOW YOU DON'T WANT TO SEND A CARD TO 'POOCHIE'
I'M GLAD YOU KNOW THAT!
KIM? RANDI? NORMA?
NOPE! NOPE! NOPE!
HOW ABOUT AMY? I THINK AMY SHOULD GET A CARD
MAYBE YOU'RE RIGHT
OKAY, IT'S SETTLED..YOU'LL SEND A CARD TO AMY...I'LL MAIL IT OUT TODAY...
THANK YOU
THAT'S THE TROUBLE WITH HAVING ONLY ONE STAMP...
SCHULZ

MY REPORT TODAY IS ON DINOSAURS...
THE LARGEST DINOSAUR THAT EVER LIVED WAS THE BRONCHITIS
IT SOON BECAME EXTINCT...
IT COUGHED A LOT!
SCHULZ

Ten milligrams equals one centigram.
Ten decigrams equals one gram.
Ten grams equals one grampa.
KEEP GOING... I CAN HARDLY WAIT TO SEE WHAT COMES NEXT...
SCHULZ

PSYCHIATRIC HELP 7¢
THE DOCTOR IS IN
I KNOW I NEED HELP... I DON'T DENY THAT..
..BUT SOMEHOW I FEEL THAT I DON'T REALLY WANT TO GO THROUGH THE WHOLE PSYCHIATRIC BIT...YOU KNOW WHAT I MEAN?
ABSOLUTELY...JUST STEP OVER HERE, PLEASE...
GOOD, SOUND, MOTHERLY ADVICE
MOM IS IN
SCHULZ

HAPPY BEETHOVEN'S BIRTHDAY! AREN'T YOU GOING TO KISS ME?
GOOD GRIEF, NO!!
BEETHOVEN WOULD HAVE WANTED YOU TO!
I DOUBT THAT VERY MUCH!
WELL, I'LL BET BRAHMS WOULD HAVE WANTED YOU TO!!
SCHULZ

I DON'T THINK I'LL TELL WOODSTOCK ABOUT SANTA CLAUS...
HE'LL NEVER GET ANY PRESENTS ANYWAY
SANTA CLAUS NEVER BRINGS PRESENTS TO TINY, NONDESCRIPT, NOBODY BIRDS
IT'S KIND OF SAD AT CHRISTMASTIME TO BE A NOBODY BIRD...
SCHULZ

WHAT I REALLY SHOULD DO IS INVITE WOODSTOCK BACK TO THE DAISY HILL PUPPY FARM FOR CHRISTMAS
HE'D LIKE THAT...IT'S FUN TO GO HOME FOR CHRISTMAS...
BUT HOW CAN YOU GO HOME FOR CHRISTMAS WHEN YOUR HOME HAS BEEN REPLACED BY A SIX-STORY PARKING GARAGE?
GEE, THAT'S SAD!
SCHULZ

Z
POOCHIE ?!
GUESS WHAT! YOU GOT A CHRISTMAS CARD FROM POOCHIE!
OH, NO!!
I'LL BET YOU DIDN'T SEND HER ONE, DID YOU?
OF COURSE, I DIDN'T... I WOULDN'T SEND POOCHIE A ROCK!
SHE WROTE A LITTLE NOTE ON THE BACK OF THE CARD...
I DON'T WANT TO HEAR IT!
"DEAR SNOOPY, I HOPE YOU HAVE A NICE CHRISTMAS...I THINK I AM GOING TO BE OUT YOUR WAY SOON...I'LL TRY TO STOP BY...SAY HELLO TO CHARLIE BROWN"

IF SHE COMES WITHIN A THOUSAND MILES OF ME, I'LL SCREAM!
IT'LL BE KIND OF NICE TO SEE POOCHIE AGAIN
SEEING POOCHIE AGAIN WOULD BE LIKE GETTING THE MUMPS TWICE!
YOU'VE NEVER FORGIVEN HER HAVE YOU?
YOU DON'T FORGIVE SOMEONE WHO DOES TO YOU WHAT SHE DID TO ME!
ANYWAY, HERE'S THE CARD..
I'LL BET SHE DOESN'T EVEN REMEMBER WHAT HAPPENED..
THAT WOULD BE JUST LIKE HER NOT TO REMEMBER...SHE'LL COME TO SEE ME, TOO... I KNOW SHE WILL..
JUST WHAT I DIDN'T NEED...A POOCHIE CHRISTMAS!
SCHULZ

POOCHIE'S HERE! SHE WANTS TO SEE YOU
I DON'T WANT TO SEE HER...NOT AFTER WHAT SHE DID TO ME..
THAT WAS A LONG TIME AGO..
I DON'T CARE... WE BEAGLES HAVE MEMORIES LIKE BEAGLES!
"THERE I WAS, AN INNOCENT LITTLE PUPPY, BOUNCING AROUND THE YARD ONE DAY...EAGER TO PLEASE..WILLING TO DO ANYTHING FOR A LITTLE AFFECTION..."

' THEN THIS LITTLE GIRL COMES ALONG...'POOCHIE' WAS HER NAME..SHE HAD A STICK IN HER HAND"
"'HI, CUTE PUPPY!' SHE SAYS. 'DO YOU WANT TO CHASE THE STICK?'"
"SO SHE THROWS THE STICK, AND I, LIKE A FOOL, GO RUNNING AFTER IT..."
"...FALLING ALL OVER MYSELF, BUMPING MY NOSE AND GETTING A MOUTHFUL OF MUD..."
"I GO RUNNING BACK WITH THE STICK, BRIGHT AND EAGER.."
"..JUST IN TIME TO SEE HER WALKING AWAY WITH AN ENGLISH SHEEP DOG!"
I'M AMAZED THAT YOU REMEMBER ALL THAT
HOW COULD I FORGET?
I STILL HAVE THE STICK!
SCHULZ

WHY COULDN'T SHE JUST STAY AWAY?
WHY DID SHE HAVE TO COME BACK?
POOCHIE, IT'S GOOD TO SEE YOU AFTER ALL THESE YEARS..
WHERE'S SNOOPY?
YOU WERE THE ONE WHO FIRST STARTED TO CALL ME CHARLIE BROWN...
I WONDER IF SNOOPY WILL REMEMBER ME...
HE'S CHANGED A LITTLE SINCE YOU LIVED AROUND HERE...

HE'S PROBABLY OUT IN THE BACK YARD AND...
I'M REALLY ANXIOUS TO SEE HIM...I REMEMBER WHAT A CUTE LITTLE PUPPY HE WAS...

SNOOPY?

SNOOPY, WHERE ARE YOU? SNOOPY?

!

THOMAS WOLFE WAS RIGHT...YOU CAN'T GO HOME AGAIN!
SCHULZ

I LOVE THE HOLIDAY SEASON!
I LIKE TO SEE PEOPLE BUYING PRESENTS AND DECORATING THEIR HOMES...I LIKE CHRISTMAS TREES, TOO
EVERYONE SHOULD HAVE A CHRISTMAS TREE... EVEN WOODSTOCK..
SCHULZ

IT SNOWED LAST NIGHT..
NOW, I CAN'T SEE A THING... SUDDENLY I'M SHUT OFF FROM THE WORLD AND ALL ITS PROBLEMS
LET'S HEAR IT FOR THE SNOW!!
SCHULZ

I JUST WANTED TO THANK YOU AGAIN FOR THE STRING OF PEARLS YOU GAVE ME FOR CHRISTMAS...
I DID NOT GIVE YOU A STRING OF PEARLS FOR CHRISTMAS..
I'LL SAY YOU DIDN'T!
SCHULZ

RING!
HI! I JUST STOPPED BY TO THANK YOU AGAIN FOR THE MINK STOLE YOU GAVE ME FOR CHRISTMAS
I DID NOT GIVE YOU A MINK STOLE FOR CHRISTMAS!
I'LL SAY YOU DIDN'T!
SCHULZ

I HATE TO SAY THIS, BUT YOU'VE BEEN VERY CRABBY SINCE CHRISTMAS
ANYONE WHO IS AT ALL SENSITIVE IS BOUND TO HAVE A POST-CHRISTMAS LETDOWN!
ISN'T BEING CRABBY AND HAVING A POST-CHRISTMAS LETDOWN REALLY THE SAME THING?
NOT AT ALL!!
SCHULZ

SHE MAY HAVE HONKED, BUT I NEVER HEARD HER!
SCHULZ

THIS IS SOME TEST
"WHO WAS CYRIL FOX? DISCUSS BRIEFLY THE BRONZE AGE"
"WHO WERE THE BEAKER PEOPLE? WHO WAS CASSIVELLAUNUS? WHO WAS CUNOBELIN? WHAT WERE THE CAUSEWAYED CAMPS?"
IT'S GUESSING TIME!
SCHULZ

WHAT DID YOU GET ON THE TEST, PATTY?
I GOT A "D MINUS"
THAT'S TOO BAD
IT DOESN'T BOTHER ME...
I'M JUST GLAD I HAVE MY HEALTH!
SCHULZ

TRUE
FALSE
!!
?
QUESTION NUMBER ONE...
TRUE!
TRUE AGAIN! FALSE!
TRUE, BY GOLLY! AND FALSE AND TRUE AND TRUE!
FALSE AGAIN!! THERE'S NO DOUBT ABOUT IT!

TRUE! THAT ONE IS ABSOLUTELY TRUE!
FALSE! FALSE! FALSE! TRUE!
OH, I SAY THIS ONE IS REALLY FALSE!!
TRUE! FALSE! TRUE! FALSE! TRUE! FALSE!
TRUE, BY GOLLY! TRUE!!
PSST! PATTY!
HUH? WHAT? WHAT'S THE MATTER? HUH?
YOU WERE GETTING KIND OF LOUD..
HOW EMBARRASSING
IT'S EASY TO GET CARRIED AWAY IN THESE TRUE OR FALSE TESTS...
SCHULZ

YOU ONLY EAT THE CENTER OF YOUR BREAD?
THAT'S THE PART I LIKE
WHAT DO YOU DO WITH THE REST OF IT?
THROW IT TO THE BIRDS...

DO YOU THINK THERE ARE OTHER PEOPLE IN OUTER SPACE?
NO! ABSOLUTELY NOT!
IF THERE WERE, THEY MOST CERTAINLY WOULD HAVE TRIED TO CONTACT ME!
THAT SETTLES THAT!
SCHULZ

DO YOU WANT TO TAKE ME TO THE SENIOR PROM?
THAT WON'T BE FOR ANOTHER TEN YEARS
I JUST WANTED TO GIVE YOU A BREAK...IN TEN YEARS I PLAN TO BE THE MOST SOUGHT-AFTER GIRL IN SCHOOL!

I HAVE NO INTENTION TO SEEK AFTER YOU..
WELL, IF YOU DO, I'LL BE STANDING BY THE DRINKING FOUNTAIN AT THE NORTH END OF THE BUILDING!!

THERE'S NO SENSE TO BEING SOUGHT AFTER IF YOU CAN'T BE FOUND!
SCHULZ